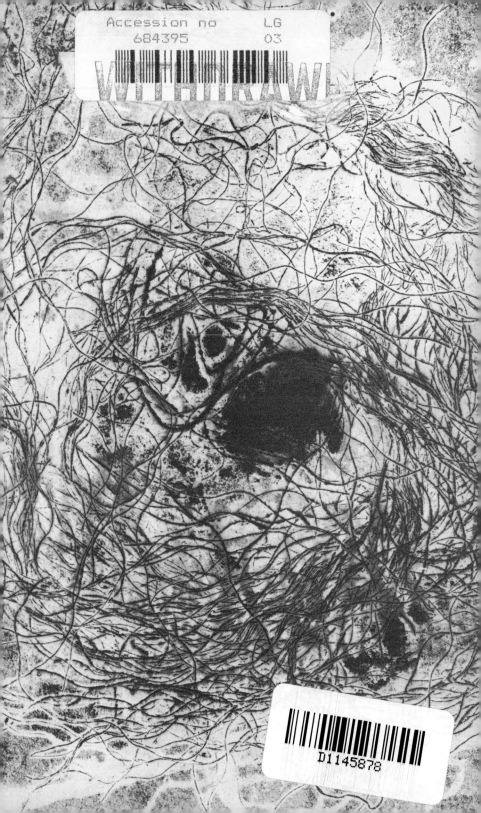

Rising early and walking in the garden
Before the sun has properly climbed the hill –
His rays warming the roof, not yet the grass
That is white with dew still.

ROBERT GRAVES
On Rising Early

RISING EARLY

Story poems and ballads of the 20th century

chosen and introduced by

CHARLES CAUSLEY

with drawings by Anne Netherwood

BROCKHAMPTON PRESS

Also by Charles Causley
FAREWELL, AGGIE WESTON
SURVIVOR'S LEAVE
UNION STREET
JOHNNY ALLELUIA
(poems)
  As editor:
PENINSULA *(West-country verse)*
DAWN AND DUSK *(poems of our time)*

First edition 1964
Copyright © 1964 Charles Causley
Published by Brockhampton Press Ltd, Market Place, Leicester
Printed in Great Britain
by Richard Clay and Company, Ltd, Bungay, Suffolk
Designer : Gerald Wilkinson
Endpaper Design : Kristina Winberg
Illustrations copyright © 1964 Brockhampton Press Ltd

TO ANTHEA AND ANTONY KAMM

CONTENTS

INTRODUCTION

Ballads and story poems came early in man's attempts at verse-making. What makes poets still write in these forms today? No poet knows exactly where his poems come from, or why at certain times he is impelled to write in a certain way. It is important to remember, too, that the poem – not the poet – chooses the physical shape and pattern it is to have. For the poet to express his thoughts and feelings in a way other than the poem demands, is to swim against a current in which he is likely to lose both himself and what he is trying to create. Robert Frost once said that a poem planned in advance never came off. 'Real ones appear unexpectedly,' added Robert Graves, 'and always at a time when the poet is in a so-called state of grace: which means a clear mind, tense heart, and no worries about fame, money, or other people, but only the excitement of a unique revelation about to be given.'

When a poet writes a story poem or ballad he addresses, per-haps, his widest audience: for, to most of us, a story is irresis-tible. As he tells it, we notice how the poet preserves the ancient virtues of this particular kind of writing. He speaks without bias or sentimentality. He doesn't seek to moralize. He allows the incidents of his story to speak for themselves; and, as we listen, we remain watchful for all kinds of ironic understatements.

No sharp boundary can be drawn between all the poems in *Rising Early* and other forms of verse, nor is one necessary. The description 'story poems and ballads' is a general one: an umbrella term. There are many ways of telling a story, and the poet is as inventive in discovering a new one as any other creative artist. What is important here is not a 'definition', a stringing together like sausages of strictly recognizable types, but the poems themselves and what they have to tell us. Broadly, I have included poems in which characters and events lie nearest the surface. The story-line in them is, I hope, fairly easily dis-tinguished and followed. As one contributor put it, the story may in one or two instances be 'subsumed' in the poem: though no less, it seems to me, than in one of the greatest ballads of all

9

time, *The Cleveland Lyke Wake Dirge*, once sung round a corpse bearing a plate or dish of salt on its breast.

> This ae night, this ae night,
> *Every night and all;*
> Fire and selte and candle-light;
> *And Christ receive thy saule.*

The fact that a poem may read simply should never deceive us as to its fundamentally deep and serious nature. If we are sensitive to the feel of such a poem, there is more than a hint of the powerful and frequently terrible currents that accompany its course, as they accompany the course of daily life. Not every word or sentiment or situation may, necessarily, be clear at a first reading. But if a work of art is something we never grow out of, or away from, perhaps this is all the better. A poem will keep something of itself permanently apart. It will always reveal, at a fresh reading, some new mystery. And it will yield only as much as the reader is prepared to bring of himself. 'A book,' said the German physicist and astronomer G. C. Lichtenberg, 'is a mirror: if an ass peers into it, you can't expect an apostle to look out.'

The poet of today, I believe, makes no attempt to 'imitate' the ballads of tradition. Rather, he has adapted freely a living form for his own needs. In some instances, for example, he may purify even more, pare to the bone, an already very spare form. Robert Graves, in *A Frosty Night* (p. 15), pushes this kind of nakedness of speech in story-telling almost to its limit.

> 'Alice, dear, what ails you,
> Dazed and lost and shaken?
> Has the chill night numbed you?
> Is it fright you have taken?'

The American poet Donald Hall, in *By the Exeter River* (p. 21), strips his story to a mere fifteen lines of dialogue.

> 'What is it you're mumbling, old Father, my Dad?
> Come drink up your soup and I'll put you to bed.'

Outside the speech, not a single word of narrative is used; the story is told entirely by hints in the conversation, with all the action taking place off-stage. In Edwin Muir's *Ballad of the Flood*

(p. 34) we are firmly at the centre of the story. But merely because the poet writes of Noah's Flood it does not mean that he turns his face from his own day, for the poem burns through time as a parable of man living for ever in the shadow of destruction. This poem, by a writer from Orkney, speaks with the voice of the North: but a reader in English in any quarter of the globe could hardly fail to respond to its central truths.

> 'Why stand ye at the window, my sons?
> What hope ye there to see?'
> 'We wad see a gudely ha', faither,
> Set in the green countrie.'

The narrative and story poems here collected generally tell, as is their function, slightly more complicated stories than those in the more straightforward ballads. The characters are developed with more subtlety, the language is usually more elaborate: though there are exceptions, for poets – very properly – are apt to adjust a form as they please. Bertold Brecht's *Children's Crusade 1939* (p. 106) moves from scene to scene now smoothly, now with deliberate jolts, but the language is always plain and stern.

> That January, in Poland
> a stray dog was caught;
> hanging from its lean neck
> a cardboard notice it brought.
>
> It read: please come and help us!
> We no longer know the way.
> There are fifty-five of us.
> The dog won't lead you astray.

In reading it, we may recall the disastrous Children's Crusade of 1212, in which something like twenty thousand children are said to have taken part. There is too another poem probably based on the same incident: Robert Browning's *The Pied Piper of Hamelin*, published in 1845; and we may consider the different manner – each, in its own way, no less effective than the other – in which the two poets, separated by nearly a hundred years, set to work on two themes that have much in common.

An 18th century Scottish patriot, Andrew Fletcher of Saltoun, wrote that he knew a very wise man who 'believed if a man were permitted to make all the ballads, he need not care who should make the laws of a nation'. This simple and subtle recognition of the poet's search for the stuff of life itself, and the way he is able to touch the rest of mankind through his work, is as true today as it was the moment the making of poetry began.

Charles Causley

Launceston, January 1964

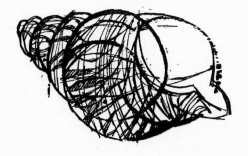

A Frosty Night

'Alice, dear, what ails you,
    Dazed and lost and shaken?
Has the chill night numbed you?
    Is it fright you have taken?'

'Mother, I am very well,
    I was never better.
Mother, do not hold me so,
    Let me write my letter.'

'Sweet, my dear, what ails you?'
    'No, but I am well.
The night was cold and frosty –
    There's no more to tell.'

'Ay, the night was frosty,
    Coldly gaped the moon,
Yet the birds seemed twittering
    Through green boughs of June.

'Soft and thick the snow lay,
    Stars danced in the sky –
Not all the lambs of May-day
    Skip so bold and high.

'Your feet were dancing, Alice,
    Seemed to dance on air,
You looked a ghost or angel
    In the star-light there.

'Your eyes were frosted star-light;
    Your heart, fire and snow.
Who was it said, "I love you"?'
    'Mother, let me go!'

ROBERT GRAVES

15

Love and a Question

A Stranger came to the door at eve,
  And he spoke the bridegroom fair.
He bore a green-white stick in his hand,
  And, for all burden, care.
He asked with the eyes more than the lips
  For a shelter for the night,
And he turned and looked at the road afar
  Without a window light.

The bridegroom came forth into the porch
  With 'Let us look at the sky,
And question what of the night to be,
  Stranger, you and I.'
The woodbine leaves littered the yard,
  The woodbine berries were blue,
Autumn, yes, winter was in the wind;
  'Stranger, I wish I knew.'

Within, the bride in the dusk alone
  Bent over the open fire,
Her face rose-red with the glowing coal
  And the thought of the heart's desire.
The bridegroom looked at the weary road,
  Yet saw but her within,
And wished her heart in a case of gold
  And pinned with a silver pin.

The bridegroom thought it little to give
  A dole of bread, a purse,
A heartfelt prayer for the poor of God,
  Or for the rich a curse;
But whether or not a man was asked
  To mar the love of two
By harboring woe in the bridal house,
  The bridegroom wished he knew.

ROBERT FROST

Bleeberrying

As Ah walked oot, yah Sunday morn,
Ta tak a wif o' t' air;
A canny lass Ah chanced ta meet,
An thus Ah spak hur fair : –
'Whor ur ye gean sa urly on ?'
Said she – 'ta Kurkstan fell,
A gedderin ripe bleeberries,
But whor ye gean yer-sel ?'

CHORUS

O hev ye geddert bleeberries,
On t' fell sides far away,
When fra abeun
Shines t' August sun
On t' fell sides far away?

Ah said ne mair but linked hur arm
In mine an off we went;
Ower many a stile, an many a bog,
An many a grassy bent;
Whor t' whinchats on a whin bush churpt,
An t' steanchats on a stean;
An t' burden o' ther merry teal
Was kiss hur ower agean.

Ah kissed hur yance, Ah kissed hur twice,
Ah kissed hur twenty times;
Ah set hur doon upon a crag
An lilted oald luive rhymes;
O, silken goons an siller croons,
An udder gramarie;
An she forgat t' ripe bleeberries
An snuggled up ta me.

Hoo blest was Ah while in my arms
Ah held hur ta my heart;
Ah laid my cheek upon hur hair,
Ah vooed we'd niver part;
Hur dark blue eyes when raised ta mine
Shone breet as t' evenin star;
Hur lips like dewy bleeberries,
An meant for me they war.

Ah've wandered many a merry mile
On folly's leetsome wing;
Ah've lontered an Ah've jigged away
Roond madcap pleasur's spring;
But t' grandest day in aw my life
Ah oft say tull me-sel
Was spent a gedderin bleeberries
Away on Kurkstan fell.

JONATHAN DENWOOD

'Bleeberries' are bilberries, or whortleberries. A fell is a mountain, or a stretch of moor. 'Whinchats on a whin bush' are small birds on a furze-bush. A 'steanchat' is a stonechat: so named because its call is like two stones struck together. 'Gramarie' is gramarye, an old word for magic, and 'lontered' means loitered.

The Evil Eye

The belief in the Evil Eye is a still-surviving superstition among Italian peasants. One method of detecting its presence is to pour olive oil on a saucer of holy water. The shapes assumed by the oil can then be read by the gifted

Nona poured oil on the water and saw the eye
    Form on my birth. Zia beat me with bay,
    Fennel, and barley to scourge the devil away.
I doubt I needed so much excuse to cry.

From Sister Maria Immaculata there came
    A crucifix, a vow of nine days' prayer,
    And a scapular stitched with virgin's hair.
The eye glowed on the water all the same.

By Felice, the midwife, I was hung with a tin
    Fish stuffed with garlic and bread crumbs.
    Three holy waters washed the breast for my gums.
Still the eye glared, wide as original sin,

On the deepest pools of women midnight-spoken
    To ward my clamoring soul from the clutch of hell,
    Lest growing I be no comfort and dying swell
More than a grave with horror. Still unbroken

The eye glared through the roosts of all their clucking.
    'Jesu,' cried Mother, 'why is he deviled so?'
    'Baptism without delay,' said Father Cosmo.
'This one is not for sprinkling but for ducking.'

So in came meat and wine and the feast was on.
    I wore a palm frond in my lace, and sewn
    To my swaddling band a hoop and three beads of bone
For the Trinity. And they ducked me and called me John.

And ate the meat and drank the wine, and the eye
   Closed on the water. All this fell between
   My first scream and first name in 1916,
The year of the war and the influenza, when I

   Was not yet ready for evil or my own name,
   Though I had one already and the other came.

JOHN CIARDI

A scapular is a small cloth badge worn on string around the neck
by religious Roman Catholics.

By the Exeter River

'What is it you're mumbling, old Father, my Dad?
 Come drink up your soup and I'll put you to bed.'

'By the Exeter River, by the river, I said.'

'Stop dreaming of rivers, old Father, my Dad,
 Or save all your dreaming till you're tucked up in bed.'

'It was cold by the river. We came in a sled.'

'It's colder to think of, old Father, my Dad,
 Than the blankets and bolsters and pillows of bed.'

'We took off his dress and the cap from his head.'

'Undressed in the winter, old Father, my Dad?
 What could you be thinking? Let's get off to bed.'

'And Sally, poor Sally I reckon is dead.'

'Was she an old sweetheart, old Father, my Dad?
 Now lean on my shoulder and come up to bed.'

'We drowned your half-brother. I remember we did.'

DONALD HALL

Burial

Nobody wanted this infant born.
    Nobody wished it dead.
They wrapped it tight as an ear of corn
    In a box of cedar and lead.

Nobody by had lighted a candle;
    No one offered to moan.
The priest and I each lifted a handle.
    The father followed alone.

Three in a Ford, that had been waiting
    Most of the wintry day.
Boys on the river still were skating;
    The wood and the road were gay :

Brown quick birds and scarlet-berried
    Twigs, and snow begun.
The priest in the back seat sat and carried
    What never saw our sun.

A blanketed horse was at the gate,
    And someone's tracks led in.
We entered, and we ascended straight
    To where the graves were thin,

And where, on a hill, the digger bent
    In wind and thickening white.
Snow covered the box that two of us leant
    To lower out of the light.

Then priestly words to cover the snow;
    The four of us stood bare.
Then clods to keep those words below.
    Now there is nothing there.

MARK VAN DOREN

The Sun came out in April

The sun came out in April,
The hawthorn in May :
We thought the year, like other years,
Would go the Christmas way.

In June we picked the clover,
And sea-shells in July :
There was no silence at the door,
No word from the sky.

A hand came out of August
And flicked his life away :
We had not time to bargain, mope,
Moralize, or pray.

Where he had been, was only
An effigy on a bed
To ask us searching questions or
Hear what we'd left unsaid.

Only that stained parchment
Set out what he had been –
A face we might have learned better,
But now must read unseen.

Thus he resigned his interest
And claims, all in a breath,
Leaving us the long office work
And winding-up of death :

The ordinary anguish,
The stairs, the awkward turn,
The bearers' hats like black mushrooms
Placed upon the lawn.

As a migrant remembers
The sting and warmth of home,
As the fruit bears out the blossom's word,
We remember him.

He loved the sun in April,
The hawthorn in May :
Our tree will not light up for him
Another Christmas Day.

C. DAY LEWIS

The Griesly Wife

'Lie still, my newly married wife,
    Lie easy as you can.
You're young and ill accustomed yet
    To sleeping with a man.'

The snow lay thick, the moon was full
    And shone across the floor.
The young wife went with never a word
    Barefooted to the door.

He up and followed sure and fast,
    The moon shone clear and white.
But before his coat was on his back
    His wife was out of sight.

He trod the trail wherever it turned
    By many a mound and scree,
And still the barefoot track led on
    And an angry man was he.

He followed fast, he followed slow,
    And still he called her name,
But only the dingoes of the hills
    Yowled back at him again.

His hair stood up along his neck,
    His angry mind was gone,
For the track of the two bare feet gave out
    And a four-foot track went on.

Her nightgown lay upon the snow
    As it might upon the sheet,
But the track that led on from where it lay
    Was never of human feet.

25

His heart turned over in his chest,
    He looked from side to side,
And he thought more of his gumwood fire
    Than he did of his griesly bride.

And first he started walking back
    And then began to run
And his quarry wheeled at the end of her track
    And hunted him in turn.

Oh, long the fire may burn for him
    And open stand the door,
And long the bed may wait empty :
    He'll not be back any more.

JOHN MANIFOLD

'Griesly' here means uncanny. Dingoes are wild or half-wild Australian dogs. A scree is a stony slope.

Birkett's Eagle

Adam Birkett took his gun
    And climbed from Wasdale Head;
He swore he could spare no more lambs
    To keep an eagle fed.

So Birkett went along the Trod
    That climbs by Gavel Neese,
Till on his right stood Gavel Crag,
    And leftward fell the screes.

The mist whirled up from Ennerdale,
    And Gavel Crag grew dim,
And from the rocks on Birkett's right
    The eagle spoke to him.

'What ails you, Adam Birkett,
    That you have climbed so far
To make an end of Lucifer,
    That was the Morning Star?

'If there's a heaven, Birkett,
    There's certainly a hell;
And he who would kill Lucifer
    Destroys himself as well.'

The mist whirled off from Gavel Crag,
    And swept towards Beck Head,
And Adam Birkett took his aim
    And shot the eagle dead.

He looked down into Ennerdale
    To where its body fell,
And at his back stood Gavel Crag,
    And at his feet lay Hell.

Birkett scrambled off the rocks,
    And back onto the Trod,
And on his right lay Ennerdale,
    And on his left stood God.

'What was it, Adam Birkett,
    That fell onto the scree?
For I feared it might be Lucifer,
    That once was dear to me.

'And from Carlisle to Ravenglass,
    From Shap to St Bees Head,
There's nobody worth vanquishing
    If Lucifer is dead.'

Birkett's dogs leapt all about
    As he came down the scree,
But he said 'I have killed Lucifer,
    And what is left for me?'

Birkett's lambs leapt all about
    As he came off the fell,
But he said 'I have killed Lucifer,
    And I am dead as well.'

But Lucifer the Morning Star
    Walked thoughtfully away
From the screes beyond the Gavel
    Where the eagle's body lay.

And as he went by Black Sail Pass
    And round below Kirk Fell,
He looked like young Tom Ritson
    Who knew the Birketts well.

And he came down to Wasdale Head,
   Young Ritson to the life,
With an apple in his pocket
   Which he gave to Birkett's wife.

DOROTHY S. HOWARD

The Young Cordwainer

SHE   Love, why have you led me here
        To this lampless hall,
    A place of despair and fear
        Where blind things crawl?

HE   Not I, but your complaint
        Heard by the riverside
    That primrose scent grew faint
        And desire died.

SHE   Kisses had lost virtue
        As yourself must know;
    I declared what, alas, was true
        And still shall do so.

HE   Mount, sweetheart, this main stair
        Where bandogs at the foot
    Their crooked gilt teeth bare
        Between jaws of soot.

SHE   I loathe them, how they stand
        Like prick-eared spies.
    Hold me fast by the left hand;
        I walk with closed eyes.

HE   Primrose has periwinkle
        As her mortal fellow:
    Five leaves, blue and baleful,
        Five of true yellow.

SHE   Overhead, what's overhead?
        Where would you take me?
    My feet stumble for dread,
        My wits forsake me.

HE   Flight on flight, floor above floor,
        In suspense of doom
    To a locked secret door
        And a white-walled room.

SHE   Love, have you the pass-word,
        Or have you the key,
    With a sharp naked sword
        And wine to revive me?

HE   Enter: here is star-light,
        Here the state bed
    Where your man lies all night
        With blue flowers garlanded.

SHE   Ah, the cool open window
        Of this confessional!
    With wine at my elbow,
    And sword beneath the pillow,
        I shall perfect all.

ROBERT GRAVES

Robert Graves adds a note to this poem: 'An ancient French ballad tells how a princess fell in love with a young cordwainer (shoemaker) who was fated to die at her hand in a bed adorned with death-flowers, namely the blue periwinkle.'

31

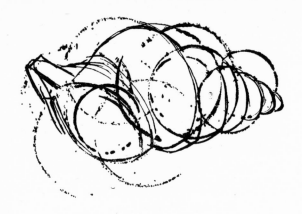

Europa

A woman one wonderful morning
    When the dew was alive on the grass
Was washing in water like quicksilver
    And laughing at herself in the glass,

At the quivering wiry wavy
    Stiffness of her vigorous hair
Which crackled as she brushed it and shook it
    Like a burning branch in the air.

Suddenly a long dark shadow
    Came in at the wide-open door
Shutting out the rhombus of sunlight
    That lay on the tessellated floor.

She saw a stately intruder
    Pause in his swaying tread
And slowly turn towards her
    A one-idea'd head,

She saw the tremendous shoulder
    And the lustrous pearly hide
And took a last look in the glass like
    A ready and summoned bride:

Stirred by the waiting monster
    And his rolling black-and-amber eye,
The enormous promise of the morning
    And the hot florescence of the sky,

She leapt on the straight flat back
    And was carried when the tide was full
Out, far out, by the Thunderer
    To sea on a great white bull.

WILLIAM PLOMER

Zeus, the greatest Greek god, fell in love with Europa, daughter of the King of Phœnicia, and came to her in the form of a white bull. After she had caressed him and leapt on his back, he carried her away to Crete.

Ballad of the Flood

'Last night I dreamed a ghastly dream,
  Before the dirl o' day.
A twining worm cam out the wast,
  Its back was like the slae.

'It ganted wide as deid men gant,
  Turned three times on its tail,
And wapped itsel the warld around
  Till ilka rock did wail.

'Its belly was blacker than the coal,
  It wapped sae close about,
That it brak the hills in pieces sma'
  And shut the heavens out.

'Repent, repent, my folk, repent,
  Repent and turn around.
The hills are sinking in the sea,
  The warld has got a stound.'

The braw lads woke beside their makes
  And drowsy were their een :
'O I wat this is anither day
  As every day has been.

'And we sall joy today, my luve,
  Sall dance to harp and horn,
And I'll devise anither play
  When we walk out the morn.

dirl o' day break of day, crack of dawn	*ilka* every
slae sloe	*stound* shock
ganted gaped	*makes* mates
wapped wrapped	*een* eyes

34

'But on the neist high day we twa
    Through the kirk door maun gae,
For sair I fear lest we sall brenn
    In living fire alway.'

They looked around on every wa'
    And drowsy were their een.
The day rase up aboon the east
    As every day had been.

But Noah took a plank o' aik,
    Anither o' the pine,
And bigged a house for a' his folk
    To sail upon the brine.

'Gang out, gang out and ca' the beasts,
    Ca' twa o' every kind
To sail upon this crackling shell
    When a' the hills are blind.

'Ca' but, ca' but, and they'll rin fast
    As sune's they hear your voice,
For they hae heard amang the hills,
    I wat, a boding noise.

'They cry a' night about the house,
    And I hae ruth to see
Sae mony innocent creatures die
    For man's iniquity.'

Noah's sons went out into the fields,
    Ca'd twa o' every kind.
They cam frae the east, they cam frae the wast,
    And followed close behind.

brenn burn	*aik* oak	*ruth* sorrow
aboon above	*bigged* built	

And some were brighter than the sun,
  Some blacker than the coal.
The lark was wiléd frae the sky,
  The serpent frae the hole.

And they were as meek as blessed sauls
  Assoilzied o' their sin,
They bowed their heids in thankfulness
  Whenas they entered in.

'Come in, come in, my people a',
  The sea has drunk the plain,
The hills are falling in the flood,
  The sun has downward gane.'

The rain it rained baith day and night
  And the wind cam together.
The water rase in a lang straight line
  Frae ae hill to the tither.

The Ark span like a cockle shell,
  Ran east and then ran wast.
'Now God us save,' auld Noah cried,
  'The warld is sinking fast.'

The beasts they hid amang the shaws
  And loud and sair cried they.
They sabbed and maned the leelang night
  And fought the leelang day,

That the creatures in the Ark were sair
  Astonied at the sound.
They trembled sae they shak the house
  As it were in a swound.

wiléd beguiled   *shaw* greenery, thicket, copse
assoilzied absolved, pardoned   *swound* fainting-fit

But syne there was nae crying mair
    Across the dowie sea.
'I wat,' said Noah, 'the warld is sunk
    Frae plain to hill-top heigh.'

The first day that auld Noah sailed
    The green trees floated by.
The second day that auld Noah sailed
    He heard a woman's cry.

And tables set wi' meats were there,
    Gowd beakers set wi' wine,
And twa lovers in a silken barge
    A-sailing on the brine.

They soomed upon the lanely sea
    And sad, sad were their een.
'O tak me in thy ship, auld man,
    And I'll please thee, I ween.'

'Haud off, haud off,' auld Noah cried,
    'Ye comena in to me!
Drown deep, drown deep, ye harlot fause,
    Ye wadna list to me.'

She wrang her hands, she kissed her make,
    She lap into the sea.
But Noah turned and laughed fu' loud:
    'To hell, I wat, gang ye!

'To hell the haill warld gangs this day,
    But and my folk sae gude.
Sail on, sail on till Ararat
    Lifts up aboon the flood.'

dowie sad   *lap* leapt
soomed swam, floated

The third day that auld Noah sailed
    There was nae sign ava'.
The water rase on every side
    Like a weel biggéd wa'.

The astonied ships upon the sea
    Tacked round and round about
Till the dragons rising frae the deep
    Sucked a' their timbers out.

Ane after ane, ane after ane,
    They sank into the sea,
And there was nane left on the earth
    But the Ark's companie.

But every day the dragons came
    And played the Ark around.
They lay upon the faem and sang;
    It was a luvely sound.

'Why stand ye at the window, my sons?
    What hope ye there to see?'
'We wad see a gudely ha', faither,
    Set in the green countrie.

'But we see naught but water, water,
    We've seen this mony a day,
And the silly fishes in the faem
    That soom around in play.'

'Sail on, sail on,' auld Noah cried,
    'Sail on, sail on alway!
I wat we'll sail about the warld
    Until the Judgment Day.'

ava' at all   *ha'* hall   *doo* dove

Noah sent a doo far owre the sea,
  It flew into the south.
It stayed four days and cam again
  Wi' a leaf within its mouth.

Noah sent a doo far owre the sea,
  It to the wast is ta'en.
It tarried late, it tarried lang,
  And cam'na back again.

'O what's yon green hill in the wast
  Set round wi' mony a tree?'
'I wat it is Mount Ararat
  New risen frae the sea.'

He's set the Ark for Ararat,
  He's plied her owre the faem,
He's lighted down at Ararat,
  And there he's made his hame.

EDWIN MUIR

39

The History of the Flood

Bang Bang Bang
Said the nails in the Ark.

It's getting rather dark
Said the nails in the Ark.

For the rain is coming down
Said the nails in the Ark.

And you're all like to drown
Said the nails in the Ark.

Dark and black as sin
Said the nails in the Ark.

So won't you all come in
Said the nails in the Ark.

But only two by two
Said the nails in the Ark.

So they came in two by two,
The elephant, the kangaroo,
And the gnu,
And the little tiny shrew.

Then the birds
Flocked in like wingéd words:
Two racket-tailed motmots, two macaws,
Two nuthatches and two
Little bright robins.

And the reptiles: the gila monster, the slow-worm,
The green mamba, the cottonmouth, and the alligator –
All squirmed in;

And after a very lengthy walk,
Two giant Galapagos tortoises.

And the insects in their hierarchies :
A queen ant, a king ant, a queen wasp, a king wasp,
A queen bee, a king bee,
And all the beetles, bugs, and mosquitoes,
Cascaded in like glittering, murmurous jewels.

But the fish had their wish;
For the rain came down.
People began to drown :
The wicked, the rich –
They gasped out bubbles of pure gold,
Which exhalations
Rose to the constellations.

So for forty days and forty nights
They were on the waste of waters
In those cramped quarters.
It was very dark, damp, and lonely.
There was nothing to see, but only
The rain which continued to drop.
It did not stop.

So Noah sent forth a Raven. The raven said 'Kark !
I will not go back to the Ark.'
The raven was footloose,
He fed on the bodies of the rich –
Rich with vitamins and goo.
They had become bloated,
And everywhere they floated.
The raven's heart was black,
He did not come back.
It was not a nice thing to do :

Which is why the raven is a token of wrath,
And creaks like a rusty gate
When he crosses your path; and Fate
Will grant you no luck that day :
The raven is fey :
You were meant to have a scare.
Fortunately in England
The raven is rather rare.

Then Noah sent forth a dove
She did not want to rove.
She longed for her love –
The other turtle dove –
(For her no other dove !)
She brought back a twig from an olive tree.
There is no more beautiful tree
Anywhere on the earth,
Even when it comes to birth
From six weeks under the sea.

She did not want to rove.
She wanted to take her rest,
And to build herself a nest
All in the olive grove.
She wanted to make love.
She thought that was the best.

The dove was not a rover;
So they knew that the rain was over.
Noah and his wife got out
(They had become rather stout)
And Japhet, Ham, and Shem.
(The same could be said of them.)
They looked up at the sky.
The earth was becoming dry.

Then the animals came ashore –
There were more of them than before:
There were two dogs and a litter of puppies;
There were a tom-cat and two tib-cats
And two litters of kittens – cats
Do not obey regulations;
And, as you might expect,
A quantity of rabbits.

God put a rainbow in the sky.
They wondered what it was for.
There had never been a rainbow before.
The rainbow was a sign;
It looked like a neon sign –
Seven colours arched in the skies:
What should it publicize?
They looked up with wondering eyes.

It advertises Mercy
Said the nails in the Ark.

Mercy Mercy Mercy
Said the nails in the Ark.

Our God is merciful
Said the nails in the Ark.

Merciful and gracious
Bang Bang Bang Bang.

JOHN HEATH-STUBBS

The Visitation

She had not held her secret long enough
To covet it but wished it shared as though
Telling would tame the terrifying moment
When she, most calm in her own afternoon,
    Felt the intrepid angel, heard
His beating wings, his voice across her prayer.

This was the thing she needed to impart,
The uncalm moment, the strange interruption,
The angel bringing pain disguised as joy,
But mixed with this was something she could share
    And not abandon, simply how
A child sprang in her like the first of seeds.

And in the stillness of that other day
The afternoon exposed its emptiness,
Shadows adrift from light, the long road turning
In a dry sequence of the sun. And she
    No apprehensive figure seemed,
Only a moving silence through the land.

And all her journeying was a caressing
Within her mind of secrets to be spoken.
The simple fact of birth soon overshadowed
The shadow of the angel. When she came
    Close to her cousin's house she kept
Only the message of her happiness.

And those two women in their quick embrace
Gazed at each other with looks undisturbed
By men or miracles. It was the child
Who laid his shadow on their afternoon
    By stirring suddenly, by bringing
Back the broad echoes of those beating wings.

ELIZABETH JENNINGS

See also St. Luke's Gospel, Chapter 1, vv. 26–56.

Peter and John

Twelve good friends
Walked under the leaves,
Binding the ends
Of the barley sheaves.

Peter and John
Lay down to sleep
Pillowed upon
A haymaker's heap.

John and Peter
Lay down to dream.
The air was sweeter
Than honey and cream.

Peter was bred
In the salty cold :
His hair was red
And his eyes were gold.

John had a mouth
Like a wing bent down :
His brow was smooth
And his eyes were brown.

Peter to slumber
Sank like a stone,
Of all their number
The bravest one.

John more slowly
Composed himself,
Young and holy
Among the Twelve.

John as he slept
Cried out in grief,
Turned and wept
On the golden leaf:

'Peter, Peter,
Stretch me your hand
Across the glitter
Of the harvest land!

'Peter, Peter,
Give me a sign!
This was a bitter
Dream of mine –

'Bitter as aloes
It parched my tongue.
Upon the gallows
My life was hung.

'Sharp it seemed
As a bloody sword.
Peter, I dreamed
I was Christ the Lord!'

Peter turned
To holy Saint John:
His body burned
In the falling sun.

In the falling sun
He burned like flame:
'John, Saint John,
I have dreamed the same!

'My bones were hung
On an elder tree;

Bells were rung
Over Galilee.

'A silver penny
Sealed each of my eyes.
Many and many
A cock crew thrice.'

When Peter's word
Was spoken and done,
'Were you Christ the Lord
In your dream?' said John.

'No,' said the other,
'That I was not.
I was our brother
Iscariot.'

ELINOR WYLIE

Ballad of the Goodly Fere

Simon Zelotes speaketh it somewhile after the Crucifixion.

Ha' we lost the goodliest fere o' all
For the priests and the gallows tree?
Aye lover he was of brawny men,
O' ships and the open sea.

When they came wi' a host to take Our Man
His smile was good to see,
'First let these go!' quo' our Goodly Fere,
'Or I'll see ye damned,' says he.

Aye he sent us out through the crossed high spears
And the scorn of his laugh rang free,
'Why took ye not me when I walked about
Alone in the town?' says he.

Oh we drunk his 'Hale' in the good red wine
When we last made company,
No capon priest was the Goodly Fere
But a man o' men was he.

I ha' seen him drive a hundred men
Wi' a bundle o' cords swung free,
That they took the high and holy house
For their pawn and treasury.

They'll no' get him a' in a book I think
Though they write it cunningly;
No mouse of the scrolls was the Goodly Fere
But aye loved the open sea.

If they think they ha' snared our Goodly Fere
They are fools to the last degree.
'I'll go to the feast,' quo' our Goodly Fere,
'Though I go to the gallows tree.'

'Ye ha' seen me heal the lame and blind,
And wake the dead,' says he,
'Ye shall see one thing to master all:
'Tis how a brave man dies on the tree.'

A son of God was the Goodly Fere
That bade us his brothers be.
I ha' seen him cow a thousand men.
I have seen him upon the tree.

He cried no cry when they drave the nails
And the blood gushed hot and free,
The hounds of the crimson sky gave tongue
But never a cry cried he.

I ha' seen him cow a thousand men
On the hills o' Galilee,
They whined as he walked out calm between,
Wi' his eyes like the grey o' the sea,

Like the sea that brooks no voyaging
With the winds unleashed and free,
Like the sea that he cowed at Genseret
Wi' twey words spoke' suddenly.

A master of men was the Goodly Fere,
A mate of the wind and sea,
If they think they ha' slain our Goodly Fere
They are fools eternally.

I ha' seen him eat o' the honey-comb
Sin' they nailed him to the tree.

EZRA POUND

A fere is a friend, mate, or companion.

St Martin and the Beggar

Martin sat young upon his bed
A budding cenobite,
Said 'Though I hold the principles
Of Christian life be right,
I cannot grow from them alone,
I must go out to fight.'

He travelled hard, he travelled far,
The light began to fail.
'Is not this act of mine,' he said,
'A cowardly betrayal,
Should I not peg my nature down
With a religious nail?'

Wind scudded on the marshland,
And, dangling at his side,
His sword soon clattered under hail:
What could he do but ride? –
There was not shelter for a dog,
The garrison far ahead.

A ship that moves on darkness
He rode across the plain,
When a brawny beggar started up
Who pulled at his rein
And leant dripping with sweat and water
Upon the horse's mane.

He glared into Martin's eyes
With eyes more wild than bold;
His hair sent rivers down his spine;
Like a fowl plucked to be sold
His flesh was grey. Martin said –
'What, naked in this cold?

'I have no food to give you,
Money would be a joke.'
Pulling his new sword from the sheath
He took his soldier's cloak
And cut it in two equal parts
With a single stroke.

Grabbing one to his shoulders,
Pinning it with his chin,
The beggar dived into the dark,
And soaking to the skin
Martin went on slowly
Until he reached an inn.

One candle on the wooden table,
The food and drink were poor,
The woman hobbled off, he ate,
Then casually before
The table stood the beggar as
If he had used the door.

Now dry for hair and flesh had been
By warm airs fanned,
Still bare but round each muscled thigh
A single golden band,
His eyes now wild with love, he held
The half cloak in his hand.

'You recognized the human need
Included yours, because
You did not hesitate, my saint,
To cut your cloak across;
But never since that moment
Did you regret the loss.

'My enemies would have turned away,
My holy toadies would
Have given all the cloak and frozen
Conscious that they were good.
But you, being a saint of men,
Gave only what you could.'

St Martin stretched his hand out
To offer from his plate,
But the beggar vanished, thinking food
Like cloaks is needless weight.
Pondering on the matter,
St Martin bent and ate.

THOM GUNN

A cenobite, or cœnobite, is a monk who is a member of a religious
community, as opposed to an anchoret or anchorite, who is a
recluse and so lives alone.

The Ghostly Father

He'd had enough of lying in the furze.
He combed gnats out of his beard,
Shrugged tendrils off his habit.

He'd try the road. But Goodness!
He was hungry, he sat, he wrung
The hem of his robe and sipped dew.

His bare feet had worn through. Thorns shivered on them,
They sank in the pasture and rattled flints
As he padded to the blot of a distant town.

He knew his face was seamed with pollen and earth,
But, peering over a smooth puddle,
Saw only the moon, blown to the full.

The trees enrolled him overhead.
A religious should not jump at shadows.
He rattled his rosary. A traveller glimpsing, ran.

This was discouraging. He sought the ditch
And burrowed through turf and fetched against bed-rock:
He would not walk, but lay blinking on packed roots;
Perhaps one day men would be more spiritual.

PETER REDGROVE

The poet writes: 'Ghostly Father has a double meaning: "spiritual parent", because he is a priest, and a real ghost too. The ghostly monk is sad when people run away, because he sees that they are not "spiritual" enough even to meet religious people, let alone ghosts. He is also mildly surprised that they should run away, for he has no reflection and cannot see himself in the puddle, only the moon behind him. "Ghostly father" as a phrase comes in both Shakespeare's Measure for Measure and Romeo and Juliet.'

Evening

Prince Absalom and Sir Rotherham Redde
Rode on a rocking-horse home to bed,

With dreams like cherries ripening big
Beneath the frondage of each wig.

In a flat field on the road to Sleep
They ride together, a-hunting sheep

That like the swan-bright fountains seem;
Their tails hang down as meek as a dream.

Prince Absalom seems a long-fleeced bush,
The heat's tabernacle, in the hush

And the glamour of eve, when buds the dew
Into bright tales that never come true;

And as he passes a cherry-tree,
Caught by his long hair, bound is he,

While all his gold fleece flows like water
Into the lap of Sir Rotherham's daughter.

Come, then, and sit upon the grass
With cherries to pelt you as bright as glass –

Vermilion bells that sound as clear
As the bright swans whose sighing you hear

When they float to their crystal death
Of water, scarcely plumed by the breath

Of air – so clear in the round leaves
They look, this crystal sound scarce grieves,

As they pelt down like tears fall'n bright
From music or some deep delight.

The gardener cut off his beard of bast
And tied up the fountain-tree, made it fast

And bound it together till who could see
Which is Prince Absalom, which is the tree?

Only his gold fleece flows like water
Into the lap of Sir Rotherham's daughter;

Sir Rotherham Redde gathers bags of gold
Instead of the cherries ruddy and cold.

EDITH SITWELL

The Biblical Prince Absalom, son of King David, was entangled
by his hair in the boughs of an oak as he rode beneath on a
mule. He was later killed by Joab and ten young soldiers while
still caught in the tree. See 2 *Samuel*, Chapter 18, vv. 9–33.

Ganga

Because its demons troubled mankind, a legendary hermit is said to have destroyed the oceans. The terrible drought that followed was ended by the saint, King Bhagīratha, whose fierce ascetic discipline persuaded the gods to release the Ganges, sacred river, from heaven. (The Rāmāyana.)

'If I hold my breath and do not speak,
If I stop my ears and my mouth and close each eye,
For the sake of the vacuum I make and the silence,
Ganga, river of God, come down from the sky.'

To reach into themselves and be no other
And whistle as they please a single tune,
Unmingled with the loud talk of the water,
Hither and thither pulled by any moon,
The springs were filled with clay, the streams diverted;
But though a city and its towers stand firm,
There are no buds or blossom on the fruit trees,
The young wheat will not quicken in the germ.

'If I suffer thirst and do not drink,
If my stomach is empty of meat and my throat is dry,
For the sake of the need I bear and the great hunger,
Ganga, river of God, come down from the sky.'

Out of the waters climbed many demons,
Coughing and laughing into the city squares,
For their knocking bones and braying conches,
No-one could sleep at night or say his prayers.
In his mountain cave the holy Brahmin
Had succubi round his mat as thick as fleas;
So hemmed about with ghostly vermin,
No wonder he cursed the rivers and wicked seas.

'If I keep my place and do not move,
If the string is taut but the arrow does not fly,
For the sake of the bent bow and the silent archer,
Ganga, river of God, come down from the sky.'

THOMAS BLACKBURN

The Rāmāyana is a great Hindu epic poem believed to be of about the year 300 BC. The 'braying conches' are the shells of molluscs used as trumpets. A Brahmin is a member of the high caste of priests among the Hindus. Succubi are female demons.

The Rise of Shivaji

'We shall cede with a brotherly embrace,'
determined Shivaji, the insurgent
king of the Marathas. Below the fortress,
Afzal Khan encamped with ten thousand men.

'We shall give in to the Emperor's will,'
spoke Shivaji to his assembled court.
'This sudden mushroom-growth below our hill
outnumbers our swords : a war would be short

'as a swim in a tempestuous sea.
We must erect cunning's dyke. Lords, nobles,
leave me with the Brahmin in privacy.
We shall pray for an end to our troubles.'

Shivaji said to the Brahmin : 'You shall
go to Afzal Khan and invite him here.
I shall embrace him by the garden wall
and resign my will to the Emperor.

'When low sunlight combs the wild jungle's hair,
I shall wait for him in my garden seat.
When the evening whispers its coolest air,
say we shall be lovers if then we meet.'

Afzal Khan encamped with ten thousand men,
deputed by the Emperor to raze
Shivaji's fame which built its monument
by stealing bricks from the empire's

walls. Afzal Khan thus answered the Brahmin's
offer of peace : 'If Shivaji accepts
defeat, then it is his reason which wins.
If our firmness, our strength he interprets

'as his weakness, then he is wise. But say
he must surrender all arms and become
a tributary which will flow always
to Delhi. If he agrees, we shall welcome

'his embrace. Say, sunset or gay sunrise,
his word we accept as of that rich hue,
our faith in it will be the butterfly's.
Say, if he loves us, we shall love him, too.'

Trumpets rang through the halls of Shivaji's court,
the Generals assembled for his speech.
'Afzal Khan has agreed to come, his escort
will be two officers. Thus, I shall reach,

'with outstretched arms and the love I profess,
his heart under the homeward flight of crows.
When we embrace, bosom to bosom pressed,
I shall sign a treaty with the tiger's claws

'on the stiff parchment of his chest. The dark
falls quickly this time of year. Each rose-bush
shall have glow-worms of my men, each tree's bark
will breathe with the secret sap of ambush.'

They sprinkled water on the lawns, his walk
towards Afzal Khan would be soft : he would
sway weakly in the air like a flower-stalk
and tip poisonous pollen into the blood

of Afzal Khan. The last crow choked his cry
when the shadows became discarded cloaks
upon the lawns. The sun, ballooned in the sky,
was about to burst. Frogs coughed their silly jokes.

Only Shivaji's men behind the trees
noticed that what burst was Afzal Khan's heart

and the short cough of hate was Shivaji's
as he unscrolled the flag of Afzal's shirt

with the gale-force of his dagger's point.
In the court, the Lords prayed, tapping the sticks
of their throats at their god. They rose then to join
in praise of Shivaji's shrewd sense of politics.

ZULFIKAR GHOSE

The murder recounted here took place in 1659. As Shivaji walked
towards Afzal Khan, he was seen to be wearing heavy rings on
the fingers of both his hands. What was not seen was that each
ring had a claw on the inside – on the palm sides of the hands.
When the two men embraced, Shivaji drove the claws into Afzal
Khan's back, and as Afzal Khan recoiled from Shivaji, he was
then stabbed in the breast with a dagger.

This is the story as Indian children used to read it at school. In
his poem Zulfikar Ghose has the 'tiger's claws' driven into Afzal
Khan from the front. Indian historians are not all agreed on the
precise manner of Afzal Khan's death.

Three Jovial Gentlemen

Three jovial gentlemen *tribes of Indians*
   Arriving with the dawn,
Down, down the mountain
   A-hunting they have gone.

One has brought a bag of salt, *band of horses*
   One a net of thongs,
Another a bow and arrow's brought.
   The taut cord thrums.

They've taken the pleasure of their craft
   In kenning and in cunning,
For the five full hours sun swelled aloft
   Kept the morning running.

Their manly mettle they've shown when
   Astride through bourne and byre
The unremitting afternoon
   Smote them with breaths of fire.

The evening's slunk in purple pall
   At their undaunted coming,
Net still empty, sack still full,
   And the bow-cord thrumming.

Night that's nipt their knuckles raw
   And smudged their clean-limned eyes
Some say surprised them on the hill.
   Some say 'twas their surprise.

Hapless, they've disarmed them, then
   Lain down to snatch their rest.
If the same dream's dreamt by several men,
   Three by one fate possessed,

Whether those wings were white or jet,
    Of metal, flame, or feather,
Those three huntsmen even yet
    Asseverate together

They've heard in her voice the peal and dole
    Of the moon and the deep tide's timbre
Gong and toll on the shell of their soul
    And their pulse rings out, 'Remember,

'Who hunts me by thought's glazened glare
    Toils to snare a shadow,
Who cleaves the dark around my bower
    Wayward as joy's arrow
Serves and masters all my power
    With incandescent marrow.'

Three jovial gentlemen
    Are rising in the dawn.
Down, down the mountain
    They hunt on, and on.

DANIEL HOFFMAN

Daniel Hoffman has written about this poem: 'Somewhere, in a book of nursery rhymes, I once came on a jingle about "Three Jovial Gentlemen" with an illustration at the head of the page showing three funny little men, in dwarf-caps and breeches, holding a lantern on a flight of stairs. I've quite forgotten how the jingle went – certainly in a different direction from the ballad that came to me years later – but the one phrase stuck in the corner of my mind. And without my in the least expecting it, the ballad got started one day.

    'The one of whom they dream (verse 9) *is* the one whose voice, in a dream, would remind each of the tide and the moon. We don't know – they don't either – exactly who she is, or what she "means", or why they dreamed of her. I leave this mysterious not to keep the secret from you, but because I believe there are joys

63

in life which cannot be captured according to a plan, or discovered by "thought's glazened glare", and perhaps not even named.

'I use the word "asseverate" (verse 8) to mean "insist upon its being the case"; the pomposity of the word is intended to have a mildly ironical effect upon how seriously we are to take the disclosure of the jovial gentlemen's dream. For we may wonder, after reading the last stanza, whether they have understood the advice they were given, or are capable of following it.'

See also the traditional ballad *The Three Jovial Welshmen*.

> There were three jovial Welshmen,
>   As I have heard men say,
> And they would go a-hunting
>   Upon St David's Day.
>
> All the day they hunted
>   And nothing could they find,
> But a ship a-sailing,
>   A-sailing with the wind.

Hunting Song

The fox he came lolloping, lolloping,
Lolloping. His eyes were bright,
His ears were high.
He was like death at the end of a string
When he came to the hollow
Log. He ran in one side
And out of the other. O
He was sly.

The hounds they came tumbling, tumbling,
Tumbling. Their heads were low,
Their eyes were red.
The sound of their breath was louder than death
When they came to the hollow
Log. They boiled at one end
But a bitch found the scent. O
They were mad.

The hunter came galloping, galloping,
Galloping. All damp was his mare
From her hooves to her mane.
His coat and his mouth were redder than death
When he came to the hollow
Log. He took in the rein
And over he went. O
He was fine.

The log he just lay there, alone in
The clearing. No fox nor hound
Nor mounted man
Saw his black round eyes in their perfect disguise
(As the ends of a hollow
Log). He watched death go through him,
Around him and over him. O
He was wise.

DONALD FINKEL

65

The Tantanoola Tiger

There in the bracken was the ominous spoor mark,
Huge, splayed, deadly, and quiet as breath,
And all around lay bloodied and dying,
Staring dumbly into their several eternities,
The rams that Mr Morphett loved as sons.

Not only at Tantanoola, but at Mount Schank
The claw welts patterned the saplings
With mysteries terrible as Egypt's demons,
More evil than the blueness of the Lakes,
And less than a mile from the homestead, too.

Sheep died more rapidly than the years
Which the tiger ruled in tooth and talk,
And it padded from Beachport to the Border,
While blood streamed down the minds of the folk
Of Mount Gambier, Tantanoola, and Casterton.

Oh this tiger was seen all right, grinning,
Yellow and gleaming with satin stripes :
Its body arched and undulated through the tea-tree :
In this land of dead volcanoes it was a flame.
It was a brightness, it was the glory of death :

It was fine, this tiger, a sweet shudder
In the heath and everlastings of the Border,
A roc bird up the ghostly ring-barked gums
Of Mingbool Swamp, a roaring fate
Descending on the mindless backs of grazing things.

Childhoods burned with its burning eyes,
Tantanoola was a magic playground word,
It rushed through young dreams like a river,
And it had lovers in Mr Morphett and Mr Marks
For the ten long hunting unbelieving years.

Troopers and blacks made safari, Africa-fashion;
Pastoral Quixotes swayed on their ambling mounts,
Lost on invisible trails. The red-faced
Young Lindsay Gordons of the Mount
Tormented their heartbeats in the rustling nights

While the tiger grew bigger, and clear as an axe.
'A circus once abandoned a tiger cub' –
This was the creed of the hunters and poets :
'A dingo that's got itself too far south'
The grey old cynics thundered in their beers;

And blows were swopped and friendships broken,
Beauty burst on a loveless and dreary people,
And their monied minds broke into singing
A myth; these soured and tasteless settlers
Were Greeks and Trojans, billabong troubadours,

Plucking their themes at the picnic races
Around the kegs in the flapping canvas booths.
On the waistcoats sharks' teeth swung in time,
And old eyes, sharply seamed and squinting,
Opened mysteriously in misty musical surprise,

Until the day Jack Heffernan made camp
By a mob of sheep on the far slope of Mount Schank,
And woke to find the tiger on its haunches,
Bigger than a mountain, love, or imagination,
Grinning lazily down on a dying ewe;

And he drew a bead and shot it through the head.
Look down, oh mourners of history, poets,
Look down on the black and breeding volcanic soil,
Lean on your fork in this potato country,
Regard the yellowed fangs and quivering claws

Of a mangy and dying Siberian wolf.
It came as a fable or a natural image

To pace the bars of these sunless minds,
A small and unimpressive common wolf
In desperately poor and cold condition.

It howled to the wattle when it swam ashore
From the wreck of the foundered *Helena*,
Smelt death and black snakes and tight lips
On every fence-post and slip-rail.
It was three foot six from head to tail.

Centuries will die like swatted blowflies
Before word of wolf will work a tremor
Of tenderness in the crusty knuckles
Around the glasses in the Tantanoola pub
Where its red bead eyes now stare towards the sun.

MAX HARRIS

A billabong is a pool near a river, sometimes caused by flooding.
There is a reference in verse 7 to the poet Adam Lindsay Gordon
(1833–1870), who joined the mounted police when he first went
to Australia at the age of 20.

A Shropshire Lad

NB – *This should be recited with a Midland accent*

Captain Webb, the swimmer and a relation by marriage of the Shropshire country novelist Mary Webb (1881–1927) was born at Dawley, in an industrial district of Salop. Matthew Webb was the first person to swim the English Channel, and crossed from Dover to Calais on 24th/25th August 1875. He was drowned in an attempt to swim the rapids beneath the Niagara Falls in 1883

The gas was on in the Institute,*
    The flare was up in the gym,
A man was running a mineral line,
    A lass was singing a hymn,
When Captain Webb the Dawley man,
    Captain Webb from Dawley,
Came swimming along in the old canal
    That carries the bricks to Lawley.
        Swimming along –
        Swimming along –
        Swimming along from Severn,
And paying a call at Dawley Bank while swimming along to Heaven.

The sun shone low on the railway line
    And over the bricks and stacks,
And in at the upstairs windows
    Of the Dawley houses' backs,
When we saw the ghost of Captain Webb,
    Webb in a water sheeting,
Come dripping along in a bathing dress
    To the Saturday evening meeting,
        Dripping along –
        Dripping along –
        To the Congregational Hall;
Dripping and still he rose over the sill and faded away in a wall.

* 'The Institute was radiant with gas.' Ch. XIX, *Boyhood*. A novel in verse by Rev. E. E. Bradford, D.D.

There wasn't a man in Oakengates
    That hadn't got hold of the tale,
And over the valley in Ironbridge,
    And round by Coalbrookdale,
How Captain Webb the Dawley man,
    Captain Webb from Dawley,
Rose rigid and dead from the old canal
    That carries the bricks to Lawley,
        Rigid and dead –
        Rigid and dead –
    To the Saturday congregation,
And paying a call at Dawley Bank on his way to his destination.

JOHN BETJEMAN

'Mineral line' is a railway-line for transporting freight only

Ula Masondo's Dream

In a gorge titanic
Of the berg volcanic
A dark cave was hidden
Long untrodden.

There leopard and snake
And tawny partridge
Prey and are preyed on,
Unstartled by cartridge,
Where never a gun
Echoing shocks
The listening rocks;
Where in winter
When the granite crags
Receive the sun,
Far down, far down,
In the sombre forest
Under thin ice
The waters splinter
In flakes of fire,
And in shallow pools
The shadow of a hawk
Tense above the tree-tops
Quivers like a fish
Among the shadows
Of basking fishes.
When those parapets shimmer
In the morning in summer
The antelope turns
From the heat of the height
To a stream in the ferns,
Bounding unhurried
From sun to shadow :
There the lory wings scarlet

73

His way at noon; twilight
Rustles with bats;
And at dawn the cliff
Frowns with eagles;
There the wild cats
Crouch and tremble,
And hear the screams
Of the furtive jackal.

The cavern is hidden
In leaves and branches:
For centuries now
No avalanches
Have scarred the steep.
The cavern can keep
Its secret in stillness,
In darkness, enfolded
In the wild fig trees,
Whose sinews are moulded
To the curves of the stone,
And whose roots are thrust
In a crevice of dust,
Clinging tightly within
To the veins of the quartz,
And fed on the secret
And tasting-of-stone
Dews of the desert,
While their leaves unshaken
Are stirred by lizards,
A refuge for spiders,
An arbour for birds,
That gouge the soft fruit
And swoop into space
With thin stabs of music
In a hollow of silence.

On windless nights
When the cave is deserted

By the last baboon
The shafted radiance
Of the risen moon
Illumines like a lamp
The vaulted roof,
Where the moss is damp
And beaded with black
Dews bled from the rock,
Illumines like the ray
White and deific
Of an enormous Eye
This tongueless place
With light terrific.
In the flare and the hush
Appear the painted
Walls. Look, the art of
Hunters who were hunted
Like beasts by men!

Now the air is tainted
With a sudden whiff
Of distant carrion,
And the silence shrills
With the urgent quills
Of vultures soaring
From their look-out cliff,
Ready to feast
On dead man or dead beast.

But the silence returns
And moonlight floats,
And the Eye returns
To men before us
In time before ours,
Whose love and hunting
Are calcined in the blaze
Of light like chalk.

Far off, far off,
Where are the savage
Cities of the future?
When these colours fade
And lichens hang in their places,
When these forms lose their graces,
When these lines are not lines,
Blighted and bitten
By the gradual acid
Of rhythmic ages,
O up then and out
And over the placid
And azure sky of midday
Will take their way
These naked hunters
With their slow-stepping women
Stained with rose-ochre
Proudly proceeding
In prancing procession
With the eland and the gnu,
While each coloured
Courser canters
With the zebra and emu,
Giraffe and zebu,
Hunters and hunted
Flying forlorn,
Faint, faded, and few,
Far off, far off,
In the equal blue.

What are you doing,
Ula Masondo?
Do you follow the Bushmen?
Are you lost in the hollow
Root of the city?

WILLIAM PLOMER

76

Ula Masondo is also the title of a story by William Plomer. In the story, a youth from Lembuland goes to Johannesburg to work in the gold-mines. One day he is trapped, deep underground, by a fall of rock. Before he is rescued he dreams of a Bushman's cave in the mountains of Lembuland. He and other boys discovered it. He had heard of the extinct Bushmen, who decorated it with paintings. The idea of their extinction becomes now mingled or confused with the idea of his own possible extinction.

'Deific' means godlike. The eland and the gnu are types of African antelope.

A Ballad of a Mine

The Wheal Owles mining disaster took place at St Just, Cornwall, on 10th January 1893, when the tin-miners broke through into an adjacent, flooded mine called Come Lucky. Nineteen men and a boy were drowned, and the sole survivor from the working where the accident took place walked the roads of West Penwith as a pedlar for the rest of his life. The shoring up of the workings with pit props is known in Cornwall as 'keeping the country abroad'. At a museum in Zennor there is a miner's lamp inscribed with the words, 'Goodbye the day. Good luck to me.'   R.S.

Between Botallack and the light
I took the lamp below,
the tunnelled summers of the mind
black and sour as sloe.
The daybreak brought the darkness down;
at day's end night was free
to dowse the lamp that carried down
'Goodbye the day. Good luck to me.'

You have to go a long way round
to have a history told.
For twenty years I've seen the lifted
white head of the road
that hills it up Nancherrow side
frown grey as a carn
and held my tongue against its spate
to keep disaster warm.

Nineteen steps up to the gate,
and half a nineteen more.
I count the steps in those men's names
who faced the waters' roar.
Nineteen years and a bit.
(The bittock was a lad.)
It goes a long way round about
to get a learned thing said.

Wheal Owles above the burning sea
that dazzles out the eye
of any man who knows the night
mine down into the day,
we bent to break the clagged ore out
while breath was harsh as scree
and sweat sloped down the buttock back.
Goodbye the day. Good luck to me.

I've never had a dream of what
the first great morning said
when the bag of water broke
for man to breach his head,
or when my father first set down
my name within his mind,
and swung his lamp down at the door
warped with the wet sea wind.

I've never had a word come in
the hollow of the dark
to tell the first great watcher's word
who broke life from the rock,
though then it was a thing enough
and all the folk stood round
as they stood at Wheal Owles the day
I got the chapter learned.

Learned me the chapter, that day did.
Nineteen paces more.
Nineteen and a bittock
from this door to that door.
What I have here I have to sell.
With breath as harsh as scree
we bent to break the black ore out.
Goodbye the day. Good luck to me.

We kept the country well abroad.
The road was clear as gin.
There was no crack or rotten tack
the working we were in.
Come Lucky nudged us on one side
but that was flooded out,
a house of water, and a house
we asked no visit at.

Come Lucky. But we have our luck.
Nineteen and a bit
your garden hedges by the road;
I've learned the length of it
from tread and tread for half a life,
the half of life let free
from mornings carrying down the shift
'Goodbye the day. Good luck to me.'

Goodbye the day. Come Lucky lay
and nudged us in the pit.
A dead man took the steel drill up
and had his luck of it.
A pinhole. But a prick, a pin.
The crack starred out like light,
light water-black. The wall of black
clapped like a Canaanite.

I often think the prophet gave
that man's discovery back.
It was a nation served by flood
that saw the splitting rock.
But we have served no waters' way
but moled below God's sea.
And on the mole the mountain fell.
Goodbye the day. Good luck to me.

Ran like a river down the latch
and sneck of deadman's door,
broke like a bag of thunderclap
upon the carn-cragged moor,
alive and kicking, wombed with flood,
nineteen and a lad
spun round, spun round, the long way round
to say their history dead.

The country was well kept abroad.
I ran through waters' house.
The great wave, shouldered like a moor,
tore all heaven loose,
and at the crack of night came luck.
The black wet let me be.
The ladder held into the shaft.
Goodbye the day. Good luck to me.

The ladder held into the shaft
and this head met the sky.
Nineteen years and a bit
I've walked the history dry.
Nineteen men and but a lad.
Did darkness break that one might see?
I learned the chapter off by heart.
Goodbye the day. Good luck to me.

ROBIN SKELTON

A bittock (verse 3) is 'a little piece'; in this case, the boy. A sneck
(verse 12) is the lever used to lift the bar of a latch. A. K.
Hamilton Jenkin, an authority on the Cornish mines, says, in a
letter: 'The cause was the more tragic since it could so easily
have been avoided. It is ascribed partly to the manager in not
keeping the Plan up to date, and in part to the men in not taking
the normal precautions when they knew they were approaching
the old workings.'

Rousecastle

Pete Rousecastle the sailor's son
From the Isle of Anglesey
Facing to the West,
Tired of the concave undercoloured sky

And of the landscapes heights afford,
Valleys, land-swelling plains,
And to be free of all
Familiar natural aspects, mountain-chains,

River-abysms, waterfalls,
And archipelagos,
Looked on the sea
Folding her waves like an unfolding rose.

81

Pete Rousecastle the sailor's son
Heard from no siren throat
The baffled, low,
Endearing, murmurous, and glutted note

Thrown by the sea to all her own.
Indeed Rousecastle saw
Only the flat
Discontinuation of a local shore.

As he walked down to the mud beach
His heart was light with an idea,
And on the horizon
Which hid beneath its straight line Africa,

The sea's familiar seaports, and
Landfalls, fixed staring eyes,
Continued on
His chosen path. The waters round him rise;

The small waves buffet him, and cling
His blue jeans jacket to his breast;
Still he walks down
The bed of ocean until the topmost

Hair of his head is under sea.
Rousecastle, sailor's son,
Now down, deep down
The hungry sea that saw his father drown,

Visits the plains of the ocean,
The glimmering country
Darker than tombs,
And unfamiliar angles of the under sea.

DAVID WRIGHT

The Ballad of Billy Rose

Outside Bristol Rovers Football Ground –
The date has gone from me, but not the day,
Nor how the dissenting flags in stiff array
Struck bravely out against the grey sky's round –

Near the Car Park then, past Austin and Ford,
Lagonda, Bentley, and a colourful patch
Of country coaches come in for the match
Was where I walked, having travelled the road

From Fishponds to watch Portsmouth in the Cup.
The Third Round, I believe. And I was filled
With the old excitement which had thrilled
Me so completely when, while growing up,

I went on Saturdays to match or fight.
Not only me; for thousands of us there
Strode forward eagerly, each man aware
Of vigorous memory, anticipating delight.

We all marched forward, all, except one man.
I saw him because he was paradoxically still,
A stone against the flood, face upright against us all,
Head bare, hoarse voice aloft. Blind as a stone.

I knew him at once despite his pathetic clothes;
Something in his stance, or his sturdy frame
Perhaps. I could even remember his name
Before I saw it on his blind-man's tray. Billy Rose.

And twenty forgetful years fell away at the sight.
Bare-kneed, dismayed, memory fled to the hub
Of Saturday violence, with friends to the Labour Club
Watching the boxing on a sawdust summer night.

The boys' enclosure close to the shabby ring
Was where we stood, clenched in a resin world,
Spoke in cool voices, lounged, were artificially bored
During minor bouts. We paid threepence to go in.

Billy Rose fought there. He was top of the bill.
So brisk a fighter, so gallant, so precise!
Trim as a tree he stood for the ceremonies,
Then turned to meet George Morgan of Tirphil.

He had no chance. Courage was not enough,
Nor tight defence. Donald Davies was sick –
We threatened his cowardice with an embarrassed kick.
Ripped across both his eyes was Rose, but we were tough

And clapped him as they wrapped his blindness up
In busy towels, applauded the wave
He gave his executioner, cheered the brave
Blind man as he cleared with a jaunty hop

The top rope. I had forgotten that day
As if it were dead for ever, yet now I saw
The flowers of punched blood on the ring floor,
As bright as his name. I do not know

How long I stood with ghosts of the wild fists
And the cries of shaken boys long dead around me,
For struck to act at last, in terror and pity
I threw some frantic money, three treacherous pence

(I cry at the memory) into his tray, and ran,
Entering the waves of the stadium like a drowning man.
Poor Billy Rose. God, he could fight
Before my three sharp coins knocked out his sight.

LESLIE NORRIS

A Rope for Harry Fat

Oh some have killed in angry love
    And some have killed in hate,
And some have killed in foreign lands
    To serve the business State.
The hangman's hands are abstract hands
    Though sudden death they bring –
'The hangman keeps our country pure,'
    Says Harry Fat the King.

Young love will kick the chairs about
    And like a rush fire burn,
Desiring what it cannot have,
    A true love in return.
Who knows what rage and darkness fall
    When lovers' thoughts grow cold?
'Whoever kills must pay the price,'
    Says Harry Fat the Old.

With violent hands a young man tries
    To mend the shape of life.
This one used a shotgun
    And that one used a knife.
And who can see the issues plain
    That rack our groaning dust?
'The Law is greater than the man,'
    Says Harry Fat the Just.

Te Whiu was too young to vote
    The prison records show :
Some thought he was too young to hang,
    Legality said No.
Who knows what fear the raupo hides
    Or where the wild duck flies?
'A trapdoor and a rope is best,'
    Says Harry Fat the Wise.

Though many a time he rolled his coat
    And on the bare boards lay,
He lies in heavy concrete now
    Until the Reckoning Day.
In linen sheet or granite aisle
    Sleep Ministers of State.
'We cannot help the idle poor,'
    Says Harry Fat the Great.

Mercy stirred like a summer wind
    The wigs and polished boots
And the long Jehovah faces
    Above their Sunday suits.
The jury was uncertain,
    The judge debated long;
'Let Justice take her rightful course,'
    Said Harry Fat the Strong.

The butcher boy and baker boy
    Were whistling in the street
When the hangman bound Te Whiu's eyes
    And strapped his hands and feet,
Who stole to buy a bicycle
    And killed in panic blood.
'The parson won his soul at length,'
    Said Harry Fat the Good.

Oh some will kill in rage and fear
    And some will kill in hate,
And some will kill in foreign lands
    To serve the master State.
Justice walks heavy in the land
    She bears a rope and shroud.
'We will not change our policy,'
    Says Harry Fat the Proud.

JAMES K. BAXTER

James Baxter writes: 'Te Whiu was a Maori lad in his late teens who was hanged for killing an old lady. It seems that she surprised him when he was burgling her house, and he killed her in a panic. He said that he needed money to buy a bicycle. He was perhaps a bit simple. He had been brought up partly by the State. I was angry about this hanging of a boy and took a petition round to try and prevent it . . .

'The "Te" is pronounced as in "when"; the "wh" as an "f"; the "i" as in "sit"; and the "u" as in "cook". By a "rush fire" (verse 2) I mean a clump of dry rushes set on fire, that blazes up and then smoulders: it does not burn for long. The leaves of the raupo (verse 4), or bulrush, were used by the Maori as thatch.'

Death on a Live Wire

Treading a field I saw afar
A laughing fellow climbing the cage
That held the grinning tensions of wire :
Alone, and no girl gave him courage,

Up he climbed on the diamond struts,
Diamond cut diamond, till he stood
With the insulators brooding like owls
And all their live wisdom if he would.

I called to him climbing and asked him to say
What thrust him into the singeing sky :
The one word he told me the wind took away,
So I shouted again, but the wind passed me by

And the gust of his answer tore at his coat
And stuck him stark on the lightning's bough;
Humanity screeched in his manacled throat
And he cracked with flame like a figure of straw.

Turning, burning, he dangled black,
A hot sun swallowing at his fork
And shaking embers out of his back,
Planting his shadow of fear in the chalk.

O then he danced an incredible dance
With soot in his sockets, hanging at heels;
Uprooted mandrakes screamed in his loins,
His legs thrashed and lashed like electric eels;

For now he embraced the talent of iron,
The white-hot ore that comes from the hill,
The Word out of which the electrons run,
The snake in the rod and the miracle;

And as he embraced it the girders turned black,
Fused metal wept and great tears ran down
Till his fingers like snails at last came unstuck
And he fell through the cage of the sun.

MICHAEL BALDWIN

At Dunwich

Fifteen churches lie here
Under the North Sea;
Forty-five years ago
The last went down the cliff.
You can see, at low tide,
A mound of masonry
Chewed like a damp bun.

In the village now (if you call
Dunwich a village now,
With a handful of houses, one street,
And a shack for Tizer and tea),
You can ask an old man
To show you the stuff they've found
On the beach when there's been a storm :

Knife-blades, buckles and rings,
Enough coins to fill an old sock,
Badges that men wore
When they'd been on pilgrimage,
Armfuls of broken pots.
People cut bread, paid cash,
Buttoned up against the cold.

Fifteen churches, and men
In thousands working at looms,
And wives brewing up stews
In great grey cooking pots.
I put out a hand and pull
A sherd from the cliff's jaws.
The sand trickles, then falls.

Nettles grow on the cliffs
In clumps as high as a house.
The houses have gone away.
Stand and look at the sea
Eating the land as it walks
Steadily treading the tops
Of fifteen churches' spires.

ANTHONY THWAITE

Anthony Thwaite writes: 'Dunwich, pronounced Dunnitch, is now a tiny hamlet on the coast of Suffolk, but it was a large and flourishing town in the Middle Ages. The North Sea has gradually destroyed it. John Stow, the sixteenth-century historian, wrote, "There hath been in the town of Donewiche, before any decay came to it, LXX (70) pryshe churches, howses of religion, hoppitalls, and chapelles, and other such lyke." But this is probably an exaggeration. Fifteen is my conservative guess.'

Ballad of the Two Tapsters

Two tapsters traded on Thames's side
When the tide of Thames ran dry.
Their swaggering barrels were big with pride,
But the wine was hard to buy.

They had corks and taps and a counter of wood
But the running wine was gone.
'The old moon's money has gone for good,
But the new moon has not shone.'

'I saw her shining, I saw her shine,'
A tapping beggar cried.
'She carried her fortune, I made it mine,
And sleep upon Thames's side.'

He told how he slept and saw in the mud
The gold and the silver lie,
And a great round barrel, huge as a flood,
Through a corner of his starved eye.

He had watched men trundle it out of the rut
And over a plank; it fell.
He heard the wine run into the butt
As the sea runs into a shell.

Two tapsters traded on Thames's side,
But the trade in the wine went ill.
They were down to their last white penny;
There were shadows and dust in the till.

'O where can we get new wine to sell,
And where can we get it soon?'
'Our barrels are dry as a swollen cork,
Though round as the round full moon.'

They fetched an empty barrel,
They rolled it upon its side.
They propped it against the window-sill
And they pushed the window wide.

Just as the dark came stealing
And the moon rose white and still,
They laid it high on its rolling rim
And left it there to fill.

In a room of fragile moonlight
Under a cask they hide,
And they soon hear mermaids singing
Like drowned men under the tide.

Asleep like rats in the yellow straw,
They dream of a sinking ship,
White horses, a wake, then slipping,
A waggoner cracking his whip.

Now from the window leaking
The flood of light seeps in.
They hear the rattle of wheels on the street
But not one rap at the Inn.

Then up leaps the younger, and leaning
Out of the window, cries:
'Here comes old Beatwind driving
With the glint of gold in his eyes.'

'O where are you going to, Beatwind?'
'To Putney's market of wine.'
'And have you got a corner on that cart of yours
For a butt or a barrel of mine?'

'What wine would it be that you might sell,
And how shall you pay the fee,

Who are banned from the vineyards of Rhine, Moselle,
Champagne and Burgundy?

O what have you got in that barrel?'
He gave them a bargaining frown.
'It will cost you the coats on your bankrupt backs
To get this barrel to town.'

> I dreamed last night of a dancing-girl
> And the bands on her arms were gold,
> But the bands on her ankles were silver:
> O what may the great cask hold?

Two tapsters laugh in the sunlight,
In the Winter sunlight cold.
'Now, waggoner, wager your cart and horse,
Here's a barrel your men won't hold.'

Then two men tried to take it,
And four, and six men tried,
But the strongest sinews seemed like straw
That floats on Atlantic's side.

> I dreamed last night of a dancing-girl
> And the bands on her arms were gold,
> But the bands on her ankles were silver:
> O what may the great cask hold?

Be warned, you Thames-side traders,
If gambling men you be,
You cannot bend to the shores of the world
Or strive with the great dark sea.

VERNON WATKINS

'I had a clear image,' writes Vernon Watkins of *The Two Tapsters*,
'of the bed of the River Thames which had run dry and was

The Parklands

Through the Parklands, through the Parklands
Of the wild and misty north,
Walked a babe of seven summers
In a maze of infant wrath.

And I wondered and I murmured,
And I stayed his restless pace,
With a courteous eye I held him
In that unfrequented place.

Questioning I drew him to me,
Touched him not, but with an eye
Full of awful adult power,
Challenged every infant sigh.

'Of what race and of what lineage,'
Questioning I held him there,
'Art thou, boy?' He answered nothing
Only stood in icy stare.

Blue his eyes, his hair a flaxen
White fell gently on the breeze,
White his hair as straw and blue
His eyes as distant summer seas.

---

covered with silver coins. The wine was hard to buy because the tapsters had run out of shillings, and the wine merchants no longer believed they would be able to pay their debts. The moon which had, in my imagination, sucked up the sea and drained the bed of the Thames, restored all this when the tapsters tipped up their barrel to receive it. When Beatwind (the driver of the vintners' cart) and his men try to lift the barrel, they are bending to lift the waters of the Earth.'

Steadfastly I gazed upon him,
Gazed upon that infant face,
Till the parted lips gave utterance
And he spake in measured pace :

'All abandoned are my father's
Parklands, and my mother's room
Houses but the subtle spider
Busy at her spinning loom.

'Dead my father, dead my mother,
Dead their son, their only child.'
'How is this when thou art living
Foolish boy, in wrath beguiled ?'

'Ask me not,' he said, and moving
Passed into the distance dim.
High the sun stood in the heavens,
But no shadow followed him.

STEVIE SMITH

Stevie Smith writes : 'The child is the child of parents who were
murdered in front of him by the Norsemen; then he was killed.
The Norsemen sacked and burnt the great house. Everybody fled
who could. The person talking to the child's ghost is as it might
be someone today, centuries after the catastrophe.'

A ghost is said to throw no shadow : hence the last line of the
poem. See also Peter Redgrove's *The Ghostly Father* and the note
on page 54.

The Ballad of Banners (1944)

Edward the Third had seven sons
    Whose names were like the blaze
That fills the western window rose
    On summer's pageant days

In solemn tombs where pilgrims kneel
    And frescoed legends fade
Under the organ-thundered vault
    Their secret bones are laid

Who once were trumpets Kings could hear
    By dark Bohemian streams
That called the English youth to cross
    The channel of their dreams

And out of bloody deeds that struck
    The dying feudal shame
In penitence and praise create
    The rainbow ghost of fame.

It is the image shall endure
    To mould the age to come
When all the props are stowed away
    And all the actors dumb

And still the ghost of Edward's reign
    From Crécy and Poitiers
Walked the exultant, wave-blessed land
    In Shakespeare's conquering years.

And still it haunts the heart today
    Though tank and aeroplane
Roar through the wasted realm of France
    Where Louis' knights were slain

Whispering of some magnificence
    Old John of Gaunt might know
How to recapture from his dream
    Six centuries ago.

What if some wind of war should blow
    With equinoctial rage
Out of the throat of time unborn
    And blast our island stage

And the great naves should tumble down
    To sink beneath the sheaves
While all the banners stained and torn
    Were lost like autumn leaves

With every painted page that told
    Of famous enterprise
And songs that took the longbowmen
    To dazzle Europe's eyes,

Would the long roll of deeds that rang
    From Wales to Aquitaine
Somewhere be stored in God's own eye?
    Or would there but remain

The vacant sky that bears no print
    Of mortal destiny
Though the alternate stars were there
    To watch all history?

JOHN LEHMANN

The poet links the Allied landings in Europe in 1944 with the Hundred Years' War, the celebration of those campaigns by Shakespeare, and the thought that a future war might destroy the memorials of the Hundred Years' War, the Elizabethan age, and the D-Day landings. 'When every *material* evidence of history has gone,' he writes, 'does it somewhere remain "stored in God's own eye"?' Verse 3 refers to the blind King of Bohemia, killed at Crécy in 1346, fighting for the French.

Two Wise Generals

'Not as Black Douglas, bannered, trumpeted,
Who hacked for the casked heart flung to the enemy,
Letting the whole air flow breakneck with blood
Till he fell astride that handful, you and I

Come, two timid and ageing generals
To parley, and to divide the territory
Upon a map, and get honour, and by
This satisfaction part with regiments whole.'

They entered the lit tent, in no hurry to grab.
Apart in darkness twinkled their armies
Like two safe towns. Thus they drank, joked, waxed wise –
So heavily medalled never need fear stab.

The treaty sealed, lands allotted (and a good third
Stuffed down their tunic fronts' private estate)
They left the empty bottle. The tent-lamp out,
They lurched away in the knee-high mist, hearing the first bird,

Towards separate camps.
                         Now, one a late dew-moth
Eyes, as he sways, among the still tents. The other roars
    'Guard!'
As a fox ducks from the silent parapet. Both
Have found their sleeping armies massacred.

TED HUGHES

A stopwatch and an ordnance map

(To Samuel Barber)

A stopwatch and an ordnance map.
At five a man fell to the ground
And the watch flew off his wrist
Like a moon struck from the earth
Marking a blank time that stares
On the tides of change beneath.
All under the olive trees.

A stopwatch and an ordnance map.
He stayed faithfully in that place
From his living comrade split
By dividers of the bullet
Opening wide the distances
Of his final loneliness.
All under the olive trees.

A stopwatch and an ordnance map.
And the bones are fixed at five
Under the moon's timelessness;
But another who lives on
Wears within his heart for ever
Space split open by the bullet.
All under the olive trees.

STEPHEN SPENDER

James Honeyman

James Honeyman was a silent child
He didn't laugh or cry;
He looked at his mother
With curiosity.

Mother came up to the nursery,
Peeped through the open door,
Saw him striking matches
Sitting on the nursery floor.

He went to the children's party,
The buns were full of cream;
Sat dissolving sugar
In his tea-cup in a dream.

On his eighth birthday
Didn't care that the day was wet
For by his bedside
Lay a ten-shilling chemistry set.

Teacher said : 'James Honeyman's
The cleverest boy we've had,
But he doesn't play with the others
And that, I think, is sad!'

While the other boys played football
He worked in the laboratory
Got a scholarship to college,
And a first-class degree.

Kept awake with black coffee,
Took to wearing glasses,
Writing a thesis
On the toxic gases.

Went out into the country,
Went by Green Line bus,
Walked on the Chilterns,
Thought about Phosphorus.

Said : 'Lewisite in its day
Was pretty decent stuff,
But under modern conditions
It's not nearly strong enough.'

His Tutor sipped his port,
Said : 'I think it's clear
That young James Honeyman's
The most brilliant man of his year.'

He got a job in research
With Imperial Alkali
Said to himself while shaving :
'I'll be famous before I die.'

His landlady said : 'Mr Honeyman,
You've only got one life,
You ought to have some fun, Sir.
You ought to find a wife.'

At Imperial Alkali
There was a girl called Doreen,
One day she cut her finger,
Asked him for iodine.

'I'm feeling faint,' she said.
He led her to a chair,
Fetched her a glass of water,
Wanted to stroke her hair.

They took a villa on the Great West Road,
Painted green and white;

On their left a United Dairy,
A cinema on their right.

At the bottom of his garden
He built a little shed.
'He's going to blow us up,'
All the neighbours said.

Doreen called down at midnight
'Jim dear, it's time for bed.'
'I'll finish my experiment
And then I'll come,' he said.

Caught influenza at Christmas,
The Doctor said : 'Go to bed.'
'I'll finish my experiment
And then I'll go,' he said.

Walked out on Sundays,
Helped to push the pram,
Said : 'I'm looking for a gas, dear;
A whiff will kill a man.

'I'm going to find it,
That's what I'm going to do.'
Doreen squeezed his hand and said :
'Jim, I believe in you.'

In the hot nights of summer
When the roses were all red
James Honeyman was working
In his little garden shed.

Came upstairs at midnight,
Kissed his sleeping son,
Held up a sealed glass test-tube,
Said : 'Look, Doreen, I've won !'

They stood together by the window,
The moon was bright and clear.
He said : 'At last I've done something
That's worthy of you, dear.'

Took a train next morning,
Went up to Whitehall
With the phial in his pocket
To show it to them all.

Sent in his card,
The officials only swore :
'Tell him we're very busy
And show him the door.'

Doreen said to the neighbours :
'Isn't it a shame ?
My husband's so clever
And they didn't know his name.'

One neighbour was sympathetic,
Her name was Mrs Flower.
She was the agent
Of a foreign power.

One evening they sat at supper,
There came a gentle knock :
'A gentleman to see Mr Honeyman.'
He stayed till eleven o'clock.

They walked down the garden together,
Down to the little shed :
'We'll see you, then, in Paris.
Good night,' the gentleman said.

The boat was nearing Dover
He looked back at Calais :

Said: 'Honeyman's N.P.C.
Will be heard of, some day.'

He was sitting in the garden
Writing notes on a pad,
Their little son was playing
Round his mother and dad.

Suddenly from the east
Some aeroplanes appeared,
Somebody screamed: 'They're bombers!
War must have been declared!'

The first bomb hit the Dairy,
The second the cinema,
The third fell in the garden
Just like a falling star.

'Oh kiss me, Mother, kiss me,
And tuck me up in bed
For Daddy's invention
Is going to choke me dead!'

'Where are you, James, where are you?
Oh put your arms around me,
For my lungs are full
Of Honeyman's N.P.C.!'

'I wish I were a salmon
Swimming in the sea,
I wish I were the dove
That coos upon the tree.'

'Oh you are not a salmon,
Oh you are not a dove;
But you invented the vapour
That is killing those you love.'

'Oh hide me in the mountains,
Oh drown me in the sea.
Lock me in the dungeon
And throw away the key.'

'Oh you can't hide in the mountains,
Oh you can't drown in the sea,
But you must die, and you know why,
By Honeyman's N.P.C.'

W. H. AUDEN

Children's Crusade 1939

In 'thirty-nine, in Poland
a bloody battle took place,
turning many a town and village
into a wilderness.

The sister lost her brother,
the wife her husband in war,
the child between fire and rubble
could find his parents no more.

From Poland no news was forthcoming
neither letter nor printed word,
but in all the Eastern countries
a curious tale can be heard.

Snow fell when they told one another
this tale in an Eastern town
of a children's crusade that started
in Poland, in 'thirty-nine.

Along the highroads in squadrons
there hungry children tripped,
and on their way picked up others
in villages gutted and stripped.

They wanted to flee from the fighting
so that the nightmare would cease
and one day at last they'd arrive in
a country where there was peace.

They had a little leader
who was their prop and stay.
This leader had one great worry :
he did not know the way.

A girl of eleven carried
a toddler of four without cease,
lacking nothing that makes a mother
but a country where there was peace.

A little Jewish boy marched in the troop,
with velvet collar and cuff,
he was used to the whitest of bread
and he fought bravely enough.

And two brothers joined this army,
each a mighty strategist,
these took an empty cottage by storm
with nothing but rain to resist.

And a lean grey fellow walked there,
by the roadside, in isolation,
and bore the burden of terrible guilt :
he came from a Nazi legation.

There was a musician among them
who in a shelled village found a drum one day
and was not allowed to strike it,
so as not to give them away.

And there was also a dog,
caught for the knife at the start,
yet later kept on as an eater
because no one had the heart.

And they had a school there also,
and a small teacher who knew how to yell,
and a pupil against the wall of a shot-up tank
as far as peac . . . learned to spell.

And there was a concert too :
by a roaring winter stream one lad

was allowed to beat the drum,
But no one heard him. Too bad.

And there was a love affair.
She was twelve, he was fifteen.
In a secluded courtyard
she combed his hair.

This love could not last long,
too cold the weather came on.
How can the little tree flower
with so much snow coming down?

And there was a war as well,
for there was another crowd beside this
and the war only came to an end
because it was meaningless.

But when the war still raged
around a shelled pointsman's hut,
suddenly, so they say, one party
found their food supply had been cut.

And when the other heard this, they sent
a man to relieve their plight
with a sack of potatoes, because
without food one cannot fight.

There was a trial too,
with a pair of candles for light,
and after much painful examining
the judge was found guilty that night.

And a funeral too: of a boy
with velvet on collar and wrist;
it was two Poles and two Germans
carried him to his rest.

Protestant, Catholic and Nazi were there
when his body to earth they were giving,
and at the end a little Socialist spoke
of the future of the living.

So there was faith and hope,
only no meat and no bread,
and let no man blame them if they stole a few things
when he offered no board or bed.

And let no man blame the needy man
who offered no bread or rice,
for with fifty to feed it's a matter
of flour, not self-sacrifice.

They made for the south in the main.
The south is where the sun
at midday, twelve o'clock sharp
lies straight in front of one.

True, they found a soldier
who wounded on fir-needles lay.
They nursed him for seven days
so he could show them the way.

He told them : To Bilgoray !
Delirious, surely, far gone,
and he died on the eighth day.
They buried him too, and moved on.

And there were sign-posts also,
though snow rubbed the writing out;
only they'd ceased to point the way,
having been turned about.

This was not for a practical joke,
but on a military ground,

and when they looked for Bilgoray
the place was not to be found.

They stood around their leader
who looked up at the snowy air
and, extending his little hand,
said, it must be over there.

Once, at night, they saw a fire,
but better not go, they decided.
Once three tanks rolled past them,
each with people inside it.

Once, too, they came to a city,
and skirted it, well out of sight;
till they'd left it well behind them
they only marched on at night.

In what used to be South-East Poland
when snow swept the landscape clean
that army of fifty-five children
was last seen.

If I close my eyes and try,
I can see them trudge on
from one shell-blasted homestead
to another shell-blasted one.

Above them, in the cloudy spaces,
I see new long trains progress,
painfully trudging in the cold wind's face,
homeless, directionless.

Looking for the country at peace,
without fire and thunder's blast,
not like that from which they have come;
and the train grows vast.

And soon in the flickering half-light
no longer the same it seemed :
other little faces I saw,
Spanish, French, yellow ones gleamed.

That January, in Poland
a stray dog was caught;
hanging from its lean neck
a cardboard notice it brought.

It read : please come and help us !
We no longer know the way.
There are fifty-five of us.
The dog won't lead you astray.

Don't shoot him dead.
Only he knows the place.
With him
our very last hope you'd efface.

The writing was in a child's hand.
By farmers it was read.
Since then a year and a half have passed.
The dog, who was starving, is dead.

BERTOLD BRECHT
translated by Michael Hamburger

The Streets of Laredo

O early one morning I walked out like Agag,
Early one morning to walk through the fire
Dodging the pythons that leaked on the pavements
With tinkle of glasses and tangle of wire;

When grimed to the eyebrows I met an old fireman
Who looked at me wryly and thus did he say :
'The streets of Laredo are closed to all traffic,
We won't never master this joker today.

'O hold the branch tightly and wield the axe brightly,
The bank is in powder, the banker's in hell,
But loot is still free on the streets of Laredo
And when we drive home we drive home on the bell.'

Then out from a doorway there sidled a cockney,
A rocking-chair rocking on top of his head :
'O fifty-five years I been feathering my love-nest
And look at it now – why, you'd sooner be dead.'

At which there arose from a wound in the asphalt,
His big wig a-smoulder, Sir Christopher Wren
Saying : 'Let them make hay of the streets of Laredo;
When your ground-rents expire I will build them again.'

Then twangling their bibles with wrath in their nostrils
From Bunhill Fields came Bunyan and Blake :
'Laredo the golden is fallen, is fallen;
Your flame shall not quench nor your thirst shall not slake.'

'I come to Laredo to find me asylum,'
Says Tom Dick and Harry the Wandering Jew;
'They tell me report at the first police station
But the station is pancaked – so what can I do ?'

112

Thus eavesdropping sadly I strolled through Laredo
Perplexed by the dicta misfortunes inspire
Till one low last whisper inveigled my earhole –
The voice of the Angel, the voice of the fire :

O late, very late, have I come to Laredo
A whimsical bride in my new scarlet dress
But at last I took pity on those who were waiting
To see my regalia and feel my caress.

Now ring the bells gaily and play the hose daily,
Put splints on your legs, put a gag on your breath;
O you streets of Laredo, you streets of Laredo,
Lay down the red carpet – My dowry is death.

LOUIS MACNEICE

Agag, King of the Amalekites, was taken alive by Saul, but his people were 'utterly destroyed . . . with the edge of the sword'. Saul also spared the best of the spoil : the sheep, oxen, and lambs. The prophet Samuel sent for the King, who 'came unto him delicately. And Agag said, Surely the bitterness of death is past. And Samuel said, As thy sword hath made women childless, so shall thy mother be childless among women. And Samuel hewed Agag in pieces before the Lord in Gilgal.' (1 Samuel 15).

Green, Green is El Aghir

Sprawled on the crates and sacks in the rear of the truck,
I was gummy-mouthed from the sun and the dust of the track,
And the two Arab soldiers I'd taken on as hitch-hikers
At a torrid petrol-dump, had been there on their hunkers
Since early morning. I said, in a kind of French
'On m'a dit, qu'il y a une belle source d'eau fraîche,
Plus loin, à El Aghir' . . .

                It was eighty more kilometres
Until round a corner we heard a splashing of waters,
And there, in a green, dark street, was a fountain with two faces
Discharging both ways, from full-throated faucets
Into basins, thence into troughs and thence into brooks.
Our negro corporal driver slammed his brakes,
And we yelped and leapt from the truck and went at the double
To fill our bidons and bottles and drink and dabble.
Then, swollen with water, we went to an inn for wine.
The Arabs came, too, though their faith might have stood between.
'After all,' they said, 'it's a boisson,' without contrition.

Green, green is El Aghir. It has a railway-station,
And the wealth of its soil has borne many another fruit,
A mairie, a school, and an elegant Salle de Fêtes.
Such blessings, as I remarked, in effect, to the waiter,
Are added unto them that have plenty of water.

NORMAN CAMERON

Death of an Aircraft

An incident of the Cretan campaign, 1941

(to George Psychoundakis)

One day on our village in the month of July
An aeroplane sank from the sea of the sky,
    White as a whale it smashed on the shore
    Bleeding oil and petrol all over the floor.

The Germans advanced in the vertical heat
To save the dead plane from the people of Crete,
    And round the glass wreck in a circus of snow
    Set seven mechanical sentries to go.

Seven stalking spiders about the sharp sun
Clicking like clockwork and each with a gun,
    But at *Come to the Cookhouse* they wheeled about
    And sat down to sausages and sauerkraut.

Down from the mountain burning so brown
Wriggled three heroes from Kastelo town,
    Deep in the sand they silently sank
    And each struck a match for a petrol-tank.

Up went the plane in a feather of fire
As the bubbling boys began to retire
    And, grey in the guardhouse, seven Berliners
    Lost their stripes as well as their dinners.

Down in the village, at murder-stations,
The Germans fell in friends and relations:
    But not a Kastelian snapped an eye
    As he spat in the air and prepared to die.

Not a Kastelian whispered a word
Dressed with the dust to be massacred,
   And squinted up at the sky with a frown
   As three bubbly boys came walking down.

One was sent to the county gaol
Too young for bullets if not for bail,
   But the other two were in prime condition
   To take on a load of ammunition.

In Archontiki they stood in the weather
Naked, hungry, chained together:
   Stark as the stones in the market-place,
   Under the eyes of the populace.

Their irons unlocked as their naked hearts
They faced the squad and their funeral-carts.
   The Captain cried, 'Before you're away
   Is there any last word you'd like to say?'

'I want no words,' said one, 'with my lead,
Only some water to cool my head.'
   'Water,' the other said, ' 's all very fine
   But I'll be taking a glass of wine.

A glass of wine for the afternoon
With permission to sing a signature-tune!'
   And he ran the *raki* down his throat
   And took a deep breath for the leading note.

But before the squad could shoot or say
Like the impala he leapt away
   Over the rifles, under the biers,
   The bullets rattling round his ears.

'Run!' they cried to the boy of stone
Who now stood there in the street alone,
    But, 'Rather than bring revenge on your head
    It is better for me to die,' he said.

The soldiers turned their machine-guns round
And shot him down with a dreadful sound
    Scrubbed his face with perpetual dark
    And rubbed it out like a pencil mark.

But his comrade slept in the olive tree
And sailed by night on the gnawing sea,
    The soldier's silver shilling earned
    And, armed like an archangel, returned.

CHARLES CAUSLEY

Carentan O Carentan

Trees in the old days used to stand
And shape a shady lane
Where lovers wandered hand in hand
Who came from Carentan.

This was the shining green canal
Where we came two by two
Walking at combat-interval.
Such trees we never knew.

The day was early June, the ground
Was soft and bright with dew.
Far away the guns did sound,
But here the sky was blue.

The sky was blue, but there a smoke
Hung still above the sea
Where the ships together spoke
To towns we could not see.

Could you have seen us through a glass
You would have said a walk
Of farmers out to turn the grass,
Each with his own hay-fork.

The watchers in their leopard suits
Waited till it was time,
And aimed between the belt and boot
And let the barrel climb.

I must lie down at once, there is
A hammer at my knee.
And call it death or cowardice,
Don't count again on me.

Everything's all right, Mother,
Everyone gets the same
At one time or another.
It's all in the game.

I never strolled, nor ever shall,
Down such a leafy lane.
I never drank in a canal,
Nor ever shall again.

There is a whistling in the leaves
And it is not the wind,
The twigs are falling from the knives
That cut men to the ground.

Tell me, Master-Sergeant,
The way to turn and shoot.
But the Sergeant's silent
That taught me how to do it.

O Captain, show us quickly
Our place upon the map.
But the Captain's sickly
And taking a long nap.

Lieutenant, what's my duty,
My place in the platoon?
He too's a sleeping beauty,
Charmed by that strange tune.

Carentan O Carentan
Before we met with you
We never yet had lost a man
Or known what death could do.

LOUIS SIMPSON

Louis Simpson writes: 'Carentan is a village in Normandy, France. During the invasion of Normandy in 1944, this village had to be taken from the Germans by the American army, for it stood on important roads. The division in which I was serving, the 101st Airborne, was assigned to capture Carentan. The fighting described in the poem took place, if I remember correctly, at some time between June 6 and June 10. The poem describes the first actual battle experience of the company in which I served.

'The German troops we faced were parachute infantry. "Leopard suits" (verse 6) refers to their camouflage uniform, with its patchwork of mustard brown, or yellow, and green, somewhat like the spots of a leopard or markings of a jaguar. Also, some of these men, the sharpshooters, were in the trees – rather like leopards.'

The Fifth Sense

A 65-year-old Cypriot Greek shepherd, Nicolis Loizou, was wounded by security forces early today. He was challenged twice; when he failed to answer, troops opened fire. A subsequent hospital examination showed that the man was deaf. NEWS ITEM, 30th December 1957

Lamps burn all the night
Here, where people must be watched and seen,
And I, a shepherd, Nicolis Loizou,
Wish for the dark, for I have been
Sure-footed in the dark, but now my sight
Stumbles among these beds, scattered white boulders,
As I lean towards my far slumbering house
With the night lying upon my shoulders.

My sight was always good,
Better than others. I could taste wine and bread
And name the field they spattered when the harvest
Broke. I could coil in the red
Scent of the fox out of a maze of wood
And grass. I could touch mist, I could touch breath.
But of my sharp senses I had only four.
The fifth one pinned me to my death.

The soldiers must have called
The word they needed : Halt. Not hearing it,
I was their failure, relaxed against the winter
Sky, the flag of their defeat.
With their five senses they could not have told
That I lacked one, and so they had to shoot.
They would fire at a rainbow if it had
A colour less than they were taught.

Christ said that when one sheep
Was lost, the rest meant nothing any more.
Here in this hospital, where others' breathing
Swings like a lantern in the polished floor
And squeezes those who cannot sleep,
I see how precious each thing is, how dear,
For I may never touch, smell, taste, or see
Again, because I could not hear.

PATRICIA BEER

Acknowledgments

Grateful acknowledgments are made to the following for permission to reproduce copyright material :

W. H. Auden and Messrs Faber & Faber Ltd for a poem from *Another Time*

Michael Baldwin and Messrs Longmans Green & Co Ltd for a poem from *Death on a Live Wire*

James K. Baxter and the Oxford University Press Ltd for a poem from *Howrah Bridge and Other Poems*

Patricia Beer and Messrs Longmans Green & Co Ltd for a poem from *Loss of the Magyar*

John Betjeman and Messrs John Murray Ltd for a poem from *Collected Poems*

Thomas Blackburn and Messrs Putnam & Co Ltd for a poem from *The Next Word*

The representatives of the late Bertold Brecht, Michael Hamburger (translator), and Messrs Methuen & Co Ltd for a poem from *Tales from the Calendar*

The representatives of the late Norman Cameron and the Hogarth Press Ltd for a poem from *The Collected Poems of Norman Cameron*

Charles Causley and Messrs Rupert Hart-Davis Ltd for a poem from *Union Street*

John Ciardi and Rutgers University Press, U.S.A., for a poem from *As If*

The representatives of the late Jonathan Denwood for a poem from *Twinter's Wedding*

Mark Van Doren and Messrs Hill & Wang Inc for a poem from *Selected Poems*

Donald Finkel and Charles Scribner's Sons for a poem from *The Clothing's New Emperor*

The representatives of the late Robert Frost and Messrs Jonathan Cape Ltd for a poem from *Collected Poems*

Zulfikar Ghose for a poem which is included in *The Loss of India*, published by Messrs Routledge & Kegan Paul Ltd

Robert Graves and International Authors NV for poems from *Collected Poems 1959*, published by Messrs Cassell & Co Ltd

Thom Gunn and Messrs Faber & Faber Ltd for a poem from *The Sense of Movement*

Donald Hall

Max Harris

John Heath-Stubbs and the Oxford University Press for a poem from *The Blue-fly in his Head*

Daniel Hoffman and the Oxford University Press Inc, New York, for a poem from *The City of Satisfactions*

Dorothy S. Howard's poem is taken from *New Poems 1955*, a PEN anthology published by Messrs Michael Joseph Ltd

Ted Hughes and Messrs Faber & Faber Ltd for a poem from *The Hawk in the Rain*

Elizabeth Jennings and Messrs André Deutsch Ltd for a poem from *A Sense of the World*

John Lehmann for a poem from *The Age of the Dragon*, published by Messrs Longmans Green & Co Ltd

C. Day Lewis and Messrs Jonathan Cape Ltd for a poem from *Collected Poems 1925–1958*.

The representatives of the late Louis MacNeice and Messrs Faber & Faber Ltd for a poem from *Collected Poems*

John Manifold and the John Day Co for a poem from *Selected Poems*

The representatives of the late Edwin Muir and Messrs Faber & Faber Ltd for a poem from *Collected Poems 1921–1958*

Leslie Norris

William Plomer and Messrs Jonathan Cape Ltd for two poems from *Collected Poems*

Ezra Pound and New Directions, New York, for a poem from *Personae*

Peter Redgrove and Messrs Routledge and Kegan Paul Ltd for a poem from *The Nature of Cold Weather*

Louis Simpson and Wesleyan University Press, Connecticut, for a poem from *A Dream of Governors*

Edith Sitwell for a poem from *Collected Poems*, published by Messrs Macmillan & Co Ltd

Robin Skelton and the Oxford University Press Ltd for a poem from *Begging the Dialect*

Stevie Smith and Messrs Longmans Green & Co Ltd for a poem from *Selected Poems*

Stephen Spender and Messrs Faber & Faber Ltd for a poem from *Collected Poems*

Anthony Thwaite

Vernon Watkins and Messrs Faber & Faber Ltd for a poem from *The Death Bell*

David Wright

The representatives of the late Elinor Wylie and Messrs Alfred Knopf Inc for a poem from *Collected Poems of Elinor Wylie*

The compiler wishes to record his particular thanks to Alice M. Bracken, of the Brockhampton Press, for her assistance in preparing this anthology for publication.

Index of First lines

Index of Poets

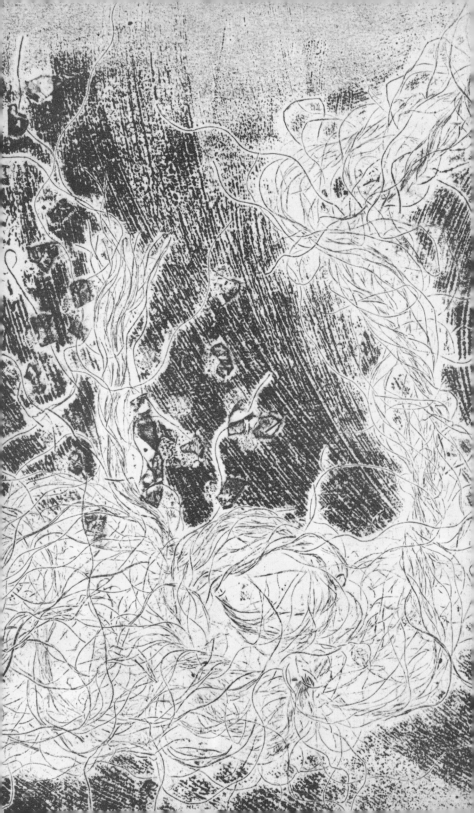